Bond Assessment Papers

Starter papers in English

Sarah Lindsay

Key words

Some special words are used in this book. You will find them picked out in **bold** in the Papers. These words are explained here.

alphabetical order	words arranged in the order found in the alphabet
antonym	a word with a meaning opposite to another word *hot – cold*
compound word	a word made up of two other words *football*
consonant letters	all letters of the alphabet apart from a, e, i, o, u (vowel letters)
noun	a word for somebody or something
proper noun	the name of a person, place, etc. *Ben*
past tense	something that has already happened
plural	more than one *cats*
prefix	a group of letters put at the beginning of a word *un, dis*
present tense	something happening now
pronoun	a word often put in place of a noun
suffix	a group of letters put at the end of a word *ly, ful*
synonym	a word with a very similar meaning to another word *quick – fast*
verb	a 'doing' or 'being' word
vowel letters	the letters a, e, i, o, u

Acknowledgements
The authors and publishers wish to thank the following for permission to use copyright material:
Jenny Dale for material from 2001 – *A Space Oddity*; Peter Dixon for 'Magic Cat'; David Harmer for 'Slick Nick's Dog's Tricks'; HarperCollins Publishers for John Jackman, 'Hippo and Monkey' from *Collins Primary Comprehension: Introductory Book* by John Jackman. Copyright © 1997 John Jackman; Trevor Harvey for 'My Eyes Are Watering'; Kingfisher Publications Plc for material from *The Kingfisher Nursery Library: Billy Goats Gruff and Other Stories*, retold by Susan Price. Copyright © Susan Price 1992; Judith Nicholls for 'The Lion and the Mouse'. Copyright © Judith Nicholls 2000; Penguin Books Ltd for material from Shirley Hughes, *Lucy and Tom's 1 2 3*, Gollancz (1987). Copyright © Shirley Hughes 1987; Steve Parker for material from *Learn about the Body*; Jo Peters for 'My Hands'; The Trustees of The Alison Uttley Literary Property Trust for material from Alison Uttley, *Hare and the Easter Eggs*, HarperCollins, pp. 6–10. Copyright © Alison Uttley Literary Property Trust 1952; A P Watt Ltd on behalf of Fox Busters Ltd for material from Dick King-Smith, 'George Starts School' from *Philibert the First and Other Stories* by Dick King-Smith, Viking (1994).

Every effort has been made to trace the copyright holders but if any have been inadvertently overlooked the publishers will be pleased to make the necessary arrangement at the first opportunity.

Paper 1

Today is Saturday. No school this morning! Lucy's clothes are on the chair in Mum and Dad's bedroom: a vest and pants, a pair of red socks, a T-shirt with stripes (first a red stripe, then a blue one, then a green), a skirt and, last of all, a pair of navy-blue shoes with red laces.

Lucy can put them all on by herself, all except for tying the laces, that is. Tom can put on his pants, one leg into each hole. But he needs a bit of help with his sweater. Which is the way out? It's all dark inside! At last he finds both the arm-holes and then out pops his head.

As soon as they are dressed Lucy and Tom go to see how Mopsa the cat is getting on. A very exciting thing happened a few weeks ago. Mopsa had kittens! She and her family are living in a box in the corner of the kitchen. It's very cosy inside with a bit of Lucy's old woolly blanket for a bed.

From *Lucy and Tom's 1 2 3* by Shirley Hughes

Underline the right answers.

1 What colour are Lucy's socks?

(red, blue, green)

2 What piece of clothing can Tom put on without help?

(socks, pants, sweater)

Answer these questions.

3 Who do Lucy and Tom go and see as soon as they are dressed?

_____

4 What makes Mopsa's box 'very cosy'?

_____

Circle the **vowel letters** in each word.

5 p l a y   6 h u n t

7–8 d o n k e y

4

Copy each sentence. Put in the missing capital letters.

9 we are going on holiday today.

_____

10 the snow covered the playground.

_____

11 harry runs very fast.

_____

12 the dog ran after the ball.

_____

4

Fill in the missing letters.

13 d e f _____ h i

14 t _____ v w x y

15 l m _____ o p

16 q r s _____ u

4

Underline the **nouns** in these sentences.

17 I bumped my head.

18 We enjoyed playing on the seesaw.

19–20 The boy dropped his book.

4

20
TOTAL

Paper 2

My Hands

Think of all my hands can do,
pick up a pin and do up a shoe,
they can help, they can hurt too,
or paint a summer sky bright blue.

They can throw and they can catch.
They clap the team that wins the match.
If I'm rough my hands can scratch.
If I'm rude my hands can snatch.

Gently, gently they can stroke,
carefully carry a glass of Coke,
tickle my best friend for a joke,
but I won't let them nip and poke.

My hands give and my hands take.
With Gran they bake a yummy cake.
They can mend but they can break.
Think of music hands can make.

By Jo Peters

Underline the right answers.

1 What do the hands in the poem paint?

(a shoe, a pin, a sky)

2 What do the hands in the poem do if they are rude?

(catch, scratch, snatch)

Answer these questions.

3 What do the hands in the poem do with Gran?

_____

4 Write about something your hands did this morning.

_____

2

2

Write a word that rhymes with the word in **bold**.

5 **hen** _____

6 **book** _____

7 **bell** _____

8 **jump** _____

Copy each sentence. Add the missing full stops.

9 The stars shone brightly in the sky

_____

10 Dan ran home as fast as he could

_____

11 The children played in the park

_____

12 Ahmed finished his homework

_____

Underline the **proper nouns**.

13–16

            David   nest   banana

   goat   Tuesday   kite   London

      gate   bridge   Scotland

Write a word with *sh* to match each picture.

17

18

_____

19

20

_____

Paper 3

Printing with paint

You will need:

- some thin sponge
- a felt-tip pen
- some glue

- a square piece of cardboard
- some thick paint
- a large piece of paper

1 Draw a simple shape on a piece of thin sponge using a felt-tip pen.

2 Cut out your shape carefully and stick it with glue on a square piece of cardboard to make a print block. Wait until the glue dries.

3 Cover the sponge on your print block with thick paint. Press the block on your piece of paper a number of times. When the paint on the sponge runs out, you can add more to continue printing.

You can make other printing blocks using different shapes cut out of thin sponge, or string dipped in glue and left to dry.

Underline the right answers.

1 What type of paint do you need to print with?

(thin, thick, doesn't matter)

2 When do you add more paint to the sponge?

(each time you print, never, when the paint runs out)

2

Answer these questions.

3 When you stick the sponge to the cardboard you should wait until the glue dries. Why do you think this is?

_____

4 Write what you think you could use your printed paper for.

Boo _____

2

Read these sentences. Write whether they happened in the **past** or are happening in the **present**.

5 Shona jumped into the puddle. _____

6 Manjit is flying his kite. _____

7 Kate walked home from school. _____

8 Elias is playing the drums. _____

4

Write a word with the opposite meaning for each of these words.

9 long _____   **10** hot _____

11 wet _____   **12** in _____

4

Put the words in the right rhyming set.

13–18

spoon   loot   noon   tool

stool   boot

root	pool	moon

6

Write two simple sentences about your school.

19 _____

20 _____

2

20
TOTAL

Paper 4

Once upon a time, there was an old woman who was baking. She made a gingerbread man for tea. She cut him out of spicy gingerbread and gave him currants for his eyes and mouth and currant buttons down his front. Then she put him in the oven to bake.

A little while later, there was a knock at the door. Not the kitchen door – the oven door! A voice shouted, "Let me out! Let me out!" So the old woman opened the oven door and *whoosh*! the gingerbread man raced past her, across the kitchen floor and out into the garden. The old woman ran after him shouting, "Come back! I baked you for tea!"

But the gingerbread man only laughed and ran on, calling, "Run, run, as fast as you can – you won't catch me, I'm the gingerbread man!"

From *The Gingerbread Man* retold by Susan Price

Underline the right answers.

1 Which meal was the old woman making the gingerbread man for?

(breakfast, lunch, tea)

2 On which door did the gingerbread man knock?

(the kitchen door, the oven door, the front door)

2

Answer these questions.

3 Where did the gingerbread man go after he left the kitchen?

_____

4 Write the reason you think the gingerbread man ran away.

_____

2

9

Write a question for each statement.

Example   Sarah had baked beans for tea.

What did Sarah have for tea?

5 Statement: Helen is seven years old.

_____

6 Statement: Tim went swimming after school.

_____

7 Statement: Liam rode his bike to Tom's.

_____

| | 3 |

Write the **plural** of each word.

8 window _____   9 swan   _____

10 train   _____   11 sister _____

12 book   _____

| | 5 |

Underline the **verb** in each sentence.

13 Stuart jumped off the wall.

14 We ran quickly through the forest.

15 Iona sat on the comfortable chair.

16 They swam to the other side of the river.

| | 4 |

Finish the sentences.

The Lewis family live in Hull. Gareth is Alice's brother. Their mother, a kind lady called Karen, helps at the local nursery. David, their father, works in the local supermarket.

17 David is Alice's f_____ .

18 Karen is Gareth's m_____ .

19 Alice is Gareth's s_____ .

20 Gareth is Alice's b_____ .

| | 4 |

| | 20 |
| TOTAL |

10

Paper 5

Your pet rabbit

Rabbits are usually friendly animals. You can get big rabbits, and small ones called dwarf rabbits. Some have ears that stand up straight and others have lop ears. They are easy pets to keep but must be kept clean and always have food and water available.

Looking after your rabbit

Every day your pet rabbit needs to be given fresh dried food and fresh water. They enjoy nibbling hay which can be bought from your local pet shop. If your rabbit lives in a hutch and doesn't have a run it is important to give it some greens from the garden. Rabbits particularly enjoy dandelion leaves. Rabbits need their hutches to be cleaned out regularly. They need clean sawdust or straw. No animal likes sleeping in a dirty bed!

Watch out!

The claws and teeth of rabbits can sometimes grow too long. If this ever happens, take your rabbit to the vet and they will trim them for you. If you don't, it could be very painful for your rabbit.

Always be careful as some rabbits are very clever at escaping and when they get out they can run very fast!

Underline the right answers.

1–2 What two things must rabbits always have available?

(food, a plastic dish, water, a brush)

3 Where should you take your rabbit if its claws grow too long?

(the garden, a pet shop, the vet)

Answer these questions.

4 What do rabbits particularly enjoy eating?

_____

5 Why is it important to clean out your rabbit's hutch regularly?

_____

3

2

Fill the gaps correctly with *was* or *were*.

6 The dog _____ taken for a walk.

7 The children _____ riding the ponies.

8 There _____ lots of swans on the river.

9 Leena _____ cooking a cake.

4

Copy the sentences and add the missing capital letters and full stops.

10 the rain soaked the children

_____

11 the park was very busy

_____

12 two ducks played in the water

_____

3

Answer these questions.

13 What colour is a post-box?   _____

14 What colour is grass?   _____

15 What colour is a carrot?   _____

16 What colour is a buttercup?   _____

4

Look at the picture and write four words with *ar*.

17 _____   18 _____

19 _____   20 _____

4

20
TOTAL

My Eyes are Watering

I've got a cold
And that is why
My eyes are watering.

It's nothing to do
With getting caught
When I planned
To SMASH
The rounders ball
SO FAR
That it would go
Into PERMANENT ORBIT
Round the school.
It would've done, too –
If Lucy Smith
Hadn't RUSHED
To catch it.

'Look at Trevor –
He's having a cry!'
Not true.
I've got a cold
And THAT is why
My eyes are watering.

OK?

By Trevor Harvey

Underline the right answers.

1 What game was Trevor playing?

(football, rounders, netball)

2 How did Trevor plan to hit the ball?

(a smash high in the air, a smash along the ground,
a smash behind him)

2

Answer these questions.

3 Who caught the ball Trevor hit?

_____

4 Do you think Trevor really had a cold? Why?

_____

Underline the **nouns**.

5–8 build   tasty   hand   table   dirty   sausage   write   kite

Do the word sums. Write the **compound words**.

9 tooth   +   brush =   _____

10 basket   +   ball   =   _____

11 lunch   +   time   =   _____

12 sand   +   castle =   _____

13 snow   +   ball   =   _____

Write these words in the order you find them in a dictionary.

dog	ant	cat	badger

14 (1) _____   **15** (2) _____

16 (3) _____   **17** (4) _____

Look at the pictures. Write in the speech bubbles what the children are saying.

18   **19–20**

Paper 7

lorry	a large vehicle that carries loads	**Mm**	
lounge	a room in a house/hotel where people sit	**magazine**	a thin book which is usually sold monthly or weekly
low	(1) close to the ground (2) feeling miserable	**magic**	in stories magic makes impossible things happen
luggage	things you take with you in suitcases or bags	**mammal**	a warm-blooded animal
lunch	a meal in the middle of the day	**mane**	long thick hair that grows on the neck of an animal
lynx	an animal in the cat family	**map**	a drawing from above of a particular area
		marble	(1) a type of hard rock that shines when polished (2) a small, coloured glass ball used to play games

Underline the right answers.

1 How many **M** words are there on this dictionary page?

(5, 6, 7)

2 Which **L** word has two meanings?

(low, lunch, luggage)

Answer these questions.

3 Which word means long thick hair? _____

4–5 Write two things a dictionary can be used for.

(1) _____

(2) _____

2

3

Write these **verbs** in the **past tense** by adding *ed*.

6 jump _____

7 kick _____

8 yell _____

9 walk _____

4

Copy this sentence and add the missing commas.

10–12 Tony bought bread milk potatoes shampoo and sweets at the shop.

_____

_____

3

Write two words ending in *ng* and two words ending in *nk*.

13–14 **ng** _____   _____

15–16 **nk** _____   _____

4

Find the four days of the week hidden in the wordsearch and write them in the spaces below.

t	h	u	r	s	d	a	y
u	f	m	k	y	s	l	o
e	q	o	p	o	s	a	p
s	u	n	d	a	y	d	n
d	o	d	y	w	w	o	d
a	f	a	e	k	e	m	u
y	r	y	u	s	d	j	y

17 _____

18 _____

19 _____

20 _____

4

20
TOTAL

Paper 8

Slick Nick's Dog's Tricks

Slick Nick's dog does tricks.
The tricks Nick's dog does are slick.
He picks up sticks, stands on bricks,
Nick's finger clicks, the dog barks SIX!
He picks a mix of doggy bix
then gives Slick Nick thick sloppy licks.
Mick and Rick's dog's not so quick –
kicks the bricks, drops the sticks,
can't bark to six, is in a fix,
gets Mick and Rick to do its tricks,
gets on their wicks despite its mix
of waggy tail and loving licks –
but Slick Nick's dog does tricks.
The tricks Nick's dog does are slick.

By David Harmer

Underline the right answers.

1 How many times does Nick's dog bark?

(four, five, six)

2 What does Mick and Rick's dog do with sticks?

(catches sticks, drops sticks, picks up sticks)

2

Answer these questions.

3 Who does Mick and Rick's dog get to do his tricks?

_____

4 Nick's dog gives him 'sloppy licks'. Write another word for 'sloppy'.

_____

2

Sort the letters to make a *th* word.

5 h n t i   _____

6 t t h e e   _____

7 r e h t e   _____

8 i k t n h   _____

4

Write a word that has a similar meaning.

9 fast _____   **10** leap _____

11 sad _____   **12** ill _____

4

Copy the sentences and add the missing capital letters.

13 At school i work very hard.

_____

14–15 i always wash my hands when i have made them dirty.

_____

16 Meena says i am her best friend.

_____

4

Underline the **proper noun** in each sentence.

17 My nanny lives in Australia.

18 My best friend is Alice.

19 I am going shopping in Stafford.

20 Imran is coming to my house for tea.

4

20
TOTAL

Paper 9

Slowly through the darkness, a dinosaur floated down from space, to my bedroom window. I sat up in bed, and stared as it came closer and closer. It landed in my back garden with a thump. I cautiously got out of bed and crept to the window to get a closer look. It was an Allosaurus! And it was coming my way! I gulped, and tried to run away, but I was frozen to the spot. As it came closer and closer, it seemed to get bigger. The Allosaurus lowered its head and its huge eyes stared at me, hard.

From *2001 – A Space Oddity* by Jenny Dale aged 9

Underline the right answers.

1 Where did the dinosaur land?

(in the bedroom, on the house, in the garden)

2 What size was the dinosaur?

(very small, small, big)

2

Answer these questions.

3 Why do you think the person in the story was 'frozen to the spot'?

_____

_____

4 What do you think might have happened next?

_____

_____

_____

_____

_____

2

How many **consonant letters** are in each of these words?

5 elephant _____

6 breakfast _____

7 Saturday _____

8 trombone _____

4

Copy these sentences and add the missing speech marks.

9 Where are we going? asked Paula.

_____

10 Come back, called Salima.

_____

11 Time to sit down, said the teacher.

_____

12 What is the time? asked Joseph.

_____

4

There are four letters missing in this alphabet. Which letters are they?

a b c d e f h i j k l n o p r s t u v x y z

13 _____   14 _____   15 _____   16 _____

4

Add a different **verb** to each of these sentences.

17 David _____ towards the swings.

18 Ilesh _____ in the muddy puddle.

19 Fiona always _____ her dog in the morning.

20 The children _____ to be first in the pool.

4

20 TOTAL

Paper 10

Snow

Small snowflakes are formed when the clouds get very cold. Snowflakes are frozen droplets of water that fall from the clouds. Each snowflake has a different pattern. If you catch one on your glove, look closely and you might see the delicate pattern of the snowflake.

Snow can be great fun. Many people enjoy throwing snowballs and building snowmen. In some countries, where there is often a lot of snow, children have their own skis. They ski to school or their friends' houses!

If there is a lot of snow it can cause some problems. It can block roads and railways, which stops people getting to work and school. It can be hard for older people to get out in the snow to do their shopping, as snow can be very slippery to walk on. Often birds and wild animals find it difficult to find their food buried under all the snow; and because it is so cold, water freezes and so birds and animals can't easily find water to drink.

Underline the right answers.

1–2 Why don't some people enjoy the snow?

(they find it hard to walk on, they can play in it,
it blocks the railways, they can ski on it)

2

Answer these questions.

3 Do you enjoy the snow? Why?

_____

_____

_____

4 When it snows, how can we help the birds and the wild animals?

_____

_____

_____

2

Add *ing* to the word. Then write it in a sentence.

5–6 sleep _____

_____

7–8 jump _____

_____

9–10 fall _____

_____

6

Add two more words to each column of the table. The words in each column must rhyme.

11–16

ie words	i–e words	y words
tie	*smile*	*spy*

6

Sort the letters to find the name of a month. Remember to make the first letter a capital letter.

17 n j e u _____

18 u y j n a r a _____

19 r i a p l _____

20 r c t o e b o _____

4

20
TOTAL

Some questions will be answered in the children's own words. Answers to these questions are given in *italics*. Any answers that seem to be in line with these should be marked correct.

Paper 1

1 red
2 pants
3 *Mopsa the cat (and her kittens)*
4 *a bit of Lucy's old woolly blanket*
5 play
6 hunt
7–8 donkey
9 **W**e are going on holiday today**.**
10 **T**he snow covered the playground**.**
11 **H**arry runs very fast**.**
12 **T**he dog ran after the ball**.**
13 g
14 u
15 n
16 t
17 I bumped my <u>head</u>.
18 We enjoyed playing on the <u>seesaw</u>.
19–20
The <u>boy</u> dropped his <u>book</u>.

Paper 2

1 a sky
2 snatch
3 they bake a yummy cake
4 *[answer stating something their hands did this morning]*
5 e.g. pen or ten
6 e.g. cook or look
7 e.g. sell or tell
8 e.g. lump or dump
9 The stars shone brightly in the sky**.**
10 Dan ran home as fast as he could**.**
11 The children played in the park**.**
12 Ahmed finished his homework**.**
13–16
David, Tuesday, London, Scotland
17 shell
18 shop
19 fish
20 dish

Paper 3

1 thick
2 when the paint runs out
3 *if you don't, the sponge will come away from the cardboard when you try to print*
4 e.g. wrapping paper
5 past
6 present
7 past
8 present
9 e.g. short
10 e.g. cold
11 e.g. dry
12 e.g. out
13–18

root	pool	moon
loot	tool	spoon
boot	stool	noon

19–20
[two simple sentences about their school]

Paper 4

1 tea
2 the oven door
3 into the garden
4 *[answer stating why they think the gingerbread man ran away]*
5 *e.g. How old is Helen?*
6 *e.g. Where did Tim go after school?*
7 *e.g. How did Liam get to Tom's?*
8 windows
9 swans
10 trains
11 sisters
12 books
13 Stuart <u>jumped</u> off the wall.
14 We <u>ran</u> quickly through the forest.
15 Iona <u>sat</u> on the comfortable chair.
16 They <u>swam</u> to the other side of the river.
17 father
18 mother
19 sister
20 brother

Paper 5

1–2 food, water
3 the vet
4 *dandelion leaves*
5 *e.g. No animal likes sleeping in a dirty bed.*
6 was
7 were
8 were
9 was
10 **T**he rain soaked the children**.**
11 **T**he park was very busy**.**
12 **T**wo ducks played in the water**.**
13 red
14 green

15 orange

16 yellow

17–20

four of the following in any order: arm, scarf, star, shark, dark

Paper 6

1 rounders

2 a smash high in the air

3 Lucy Smith

4 *[answer stating that they don't think Trevor had a cold, he was upset about Lucy catching the ball]*

5–8 hand, table, sausage, kite

9 toothbrush

10 basketball

11 lunchtime

12 sandcastle

13 snowball

14 ant

15 badger

16 cat

17 dog

18–20

[speech bubbles with appropriate conversation between the children]

Paper 7

1 6

2 low

3 *mane*

4–5 *e.g. (1) to check how to spell words*
e.g. (2) to find out what words mean

6 jumped

7 kicked

8 yelled

9 walked

10–12

Tony bought bread**,** milk, potatoes, shampoo and

sweets at the shop.

13–14

e.g. sing, ring

15–16

e.g. bank, tank

17–20

any order: Monday, Tuesday, Thursday, Sunday

Paper 8

1 six

2 drops sticks

3 Mick and Rick

4 e.g. wet

5 thin

6 teeth

7 three or there

8 think

9 e.g. quick

10 e.g. jump

11 e.g. unhappy or miserable

12 e.g. sick or unwell or poorly

13 At school **I** work very hard.

14–15

I always wash my hands when **I** have made them dirty.

16 Meena says **I** am her best friend.

17 My nanny lives in Australia.

18 My best friend is Alice.

19 I am going shopping in Stafford.

20 Imran is coming to my house for tea.

Paper 9

1 in the garden

2 big

3 *because he/she was very scared*

4 *[answer stating what they*

think happened next]

5 5

6 6

7 5

8 5

9 "Where are we going?" asked Paula.

10 "Come back," called Salima.

11 "Time to sit down," said the teacher.

12 "What is the time?" asked Joseph.

13–16

a b c d e f **g** h i j k l **m** n o p **q** r s t u v **w** x y z

17 e.g. ran

18 e.g. jumped

19 e.g. brushed

20 e.g. rushed

Paper 10

1–2 they find it hard to walk on, it blocks the railways

3 *[answer stating whether they enjoy the snow and why]*

4 *[answer suggesting birds and wild animals can be helped by providing water and food when it snows]*

5–6 sleeping *[sentence including the word sleeping]*

7–8 jumping *[sentence including the word jumping]*

9–10

falling *[sentence including the word falling]*

11–16

ie words	i-e words	y words
tie	smile	spy
e.g. lie	e.g. pile	e.g. fly
e.g. pie	e.g. mile	e.g. sky

17 June
18 January
19 April
20 October

Paper 11

1 a cowslip
2 the chocolate eggs
3 His fur quivered, and his heart thumped.
4 *[answer stating what they think happens next]*
5 during
6 after
7 then
8 before
9 quietly
10 quickly
11 smartly
12 safely
13–14
  The children went to the dentist**.**
15–17
  One morning **J**acob met a strange-looking lizard**.**
18 pencil
19 rubber
20 sharpener

Paper 12

1 Hippo
2 no
3 *he was strong, grumpy and moody*
4 *[answer stating what they think Monkey said next]*
5 black
6 purple
7 brown
8 green
9–11
  When we went swimming we had to remember a towel, a drink, our

swimming costume, a brush and some money.
12–13
  cr**ow**   b**oa**t
14–15
  t**oe**   bl**ow**
16–17
  g**oa**t   d**oe**
18 Ten children **are** playing on the climbing frame.
19 Lucy **is** going to Paul's house for tea.
20 Adele and Tony **are** going on holiday.

Paper 13

1 5
2 accidents and bones
3 *a book on caring for dogs*
4 J and O
5–10

Fishing	Cooking
rod	mixing bowl
maggots	dried fruit
waterproof clothing	oven

11 Ali passed **him** the ball.
12–13
  We saw **her** at the shops.
14 The scarf looked like **hers**.
15–16
  [Two question sentences beginning with 'When will ...' and 'What does ...']
17–18
  e.g. child, chick
19–20
  e.g. patch, watch

Paper 14

1 he was hungry
2 creatures
3 *e.g. he nibbled the hunter's net to set the lion free*
4 *e.g. weak things have*

hidden strengths and vice versa
5–9

Present tense	Past tense
dig	dug
give	gave
say	said
tell	told
grow	grew

10 sl**ee**p
11 str**eam**
12 sh**ee**p
13 scr**eam**
14 **T**he **R**iver **T**hames
15 **J**ack **D**resses **U**p!
16 **D**inosaurs in **W**ater
17 clean – dirty
18 hard – soft
19 shut – open
20 walk – run

Paper 15

1 an insect
2 instrument
3 instrument
4 jerk
5 *e.g. What time did Brian go swimming?*
6 *e.g. Whose house did Alice go to for tea?*
7 *e.g. What colour jumper did Mum wear on Tuesday?*
8 *e.g. When is the school fête?*
9 helpful
10 painful
11 careful
12 wonderful
13 crawl
14 run
15 swim
16 walk
17 <u>Yasmin</u> enjoyed swimming.

A3

18 We went to <u>Birmingham</u>.
19 <u>Jess</u> lives in a caravan.
20 I went to visit my grandparents in <u>India</u>.

Paper 16

1 science test
2 for behaving childishly
3–4 *e.g. assured, clever*
5–6 *(1) e.g. because he had had a tiring week*
(2) e.g. because he had been crying so much
7 boots
8 jumpers
9 farms
10 lamps
11–12
The horse jumped over the gate, the hay bail, Jacob's bike and then escaped onto the road.
13 Fiona <u>swam</u> for forty minutes.
14 Tuhil <u>kicked</u> his ball hard.
15 The ducklings <u>waddled</u> onto the grass.
16 Lara <u>lost</u> her homework.
17 Once upon a time a king lost his crown.
18 While he was searching he found his glasses.
19 Then he found the robe he lost last year.
20 In the end he found his crown; he had left it in the bathroom!

Paper 17

1 a jelly-like material
2 the back legs
3 11 weeks
4 *e.g. for food, for protection*
5 train
6 spray

7 tray
8 snail
9–12
[four questions, one each beginning with Where, When, What and Which]
13–16
any order: teacher, table, paint, book
17–20
[four sentences, each one including one of the following words – before, next, during, meanwhile]

Paper 18

1 big wings
2 the cat
3 beneath
4 *[answer stating whether they think Tibby liked having the magic spilt on her and why]*
5 **S**chool **S**tories
6 **T**he **B**adger's **B**ath
7 **F**amous **P**eople in **H**istory
8 **G**rowing a **S**unflower
9 dislike
10 disobey
11 disappear
12 distrust
13 e.g. teacher, playground, assembly
14 e.g. goal, referee, players
15 e.g. bride, groom, church
16 e.g. paintbrush, paint, paper
17 fighting
18 bending
19 throwing
20 helping

Paper 19

1 no
2 nose

3 *e.g. scared*
4 *e.g. you look in a mirror more often at your face than any other part of your body – brushing teeth, etc.*
5–6 The **dog** <u>swam</u> in the **river**.
7–8 We <u>ate</u> some **sweets**.
9–10
They <u>jumped</u> onto the **wall**.
11 We must put our coats on.
12 Where is my hat?
13 It is cold outside.
14 dolphin
15 wheel
16 elephant
17 white
18 e.g. fast
19 e.g. munch
20 e.g. yell

Paper 20

1 one shilling
2 on the hill
3 *so they could get married*
4 *[answer stating favourite verse and why]*
5 curry
6 mushrooms
7 pizza
8 sausages
9–11
"Please come to my house for tea," said Clare.
12–14
"When shall I come to tea**?**" asked Jess.
15–17
b<u>ir</u>d p<u>ur</u>se n<u>er</u>ve
18 **I** went to the shop.
19 **They** ate bananas.
20 Can **we** go swimming?

One evening in Spring, Hare was dancing along the fields, skipping and tripping and bowing to the rabbits. It was the month of March and he was feeling excited and wild, for all hares are mad in March.

"I'll go to the village," said he. "I'll go and see what there is to be seen and tell them at home all about it. I feel very brave tonight."

He stuck a primrose in his coat for luck and a cowslip in his collar for bravery, and he cut a hazel switch with catkins dangling from it, just in case.

"I'll look at the village shop and see if Mrs Bunting and the shop-bell are still there."

It was dusk when he reached the village and the children were indoors having tea. Not even a dog or cat was to be seen. Hare leapt softly and swiftly down the cobbled street.

He gave a chirrup of joy when he saw that the shop was still open. Jars of sweets in the window shone with many colours in the light of the lamp.

Hare crept close. It was a lovely sight! Whips and tops, dolls and toy horses, cakes and buns were there.

Then he opened his eyes very wide, for he saw something strange. On a dish lay a pile of chocolate eggs with sugary flowers and 'Happy Easter' written on them. Ribbons were tied round them in blue, pink and yellow bows.

"Eggs! 'Normous eggs!" whispered Hare.

He stared and licked his lips.

"What kind of hen lays these pretty eggs? I should like to take Grey Rabbit one, and Squirrel one and me one."

He pressed closer to the glass and his long ears flapped against the pane. Just then footsteps came down the street, and he slipped into the shadows and crouched there dark as night. His fur quivered and his heart thumped.

From *Hare and the Easter Eggs* by Alison Uttley

Underline the right answers.

1 What did Hare take with him for bravery?

(a primrose, a cowslip, catkins)

2 What did Hare find most interesting in the shop window?

(the sweets, the toy horses, the chocolate eggs)

2

Answer these questions.

3 When footsteps came down the street Hare was frightened. Copy the sentence that describes how frightened Hare was.

_____

4 What do you think happens next in this story?

_____

_____

Add a word from the box to each sentence. Use each word only once.

then	during	after	before

5 Adam continued to work _____ his lunchtime.

6 Salima dried her hair _____ she had washed it.

7 First Helen washed the dishes _____ she dried them.

8 Janu ate her breakfast _____ she left for school.

Add the **suffix** *ly* to these words.

9 quiet + ly = _____   **10** quick + ly = _____

11 smart + ly = _____   **12** safe + ly = _____

Copy each sentence and add the missing capital letters and full stops.

13–14 the children went to the dentist

_____

15–17 one morning jacob met a strange-looking lizard

_____

Put these words in **alphabetical order**.

rubber   **pencil**   **sharpener**

18 (1) _____   **19** (2) _____   **20** (3) _____

Paper 12

*Hippo was the strongest of all the animals, so he said he should be Chief.
The other animals didn't want Hippo as their Chief. He was too grumpy and
moody.*

"I bet I can get you out of the pool, Hippo," called Monkey.

"I bet you can't," grunted Hippo. "I'm the strongest animal in the
world."

"If I can get you out of the pool, then I should be Chief," said
Monkey.

"If you can get me out of the pool, then you can be Chief," said
Hippo, "but if I get you into the pool, you will be my servant - for ever!"

Off went Monkey to get a really strong rope.

"Hold tight to the rope," said Monkey, "but don't pull until I shout."

Monkey ran into the trees with the other end of the rope. All the
animals watched. Monkey tied the rope to a big, strong tree trunk.

"Pull!" shouted Monkey. "Pull!"

"This will be easy," thought Hippo to himself.

But all day and all night Hippo pulled, while Monkey sat and ate
bananas, and snoozed! Hippo was getting very tired and cross, very cross
indeed.

"That monkey must be the strongest monkey I've ever known,"
thought Hippo.

Slowly he climbed out of the pool, to try to see Monkey.

Just as Hippo took his last foot out of the pool, Monkey ran out of the
trees ...

Hippo and Monkey, a Nigerian folk tale retold by John Jackman

Underline the right answers.

1 Which animal was the strongest?

(Monkey, Hippo, another animal)

2 When Hippo was pulling the rope, could he see Monkey?

(yes, no)

2

Answer these questions.

3 Write a description of what Hippo was like.

_____

_____

4 What do you think Monkey ran out of the trees to say to Hippo?

_____

_____

2

Sort the letters to find a colour.

5 b c a l k   _____

6 u p r e l p   _____

7 r o n b w   _____

8 e n e g r   _____

4

Finish the sentence below with the things on the list. Don't forget the commas.

Things to remember:
towel
drink
swimming costume
brush
money

9–11 When we went swimming we had to remember a _____

_____

3

Underline the part of each word that sounds the same.

12–13 crow   boat   **14–15** toe   blow   **16–17** goat   doe

6

Fill the gaps correctly with *is* or *are*.

18 Ten children _____ playing on the climbing frame.

19 Lucy _____ going to Paul's house for tea.

20 Adele and Tony _____ going on holiday.

3

20
TOTAL

Paper 13

Underline the right answers.

1 On which page of the book would you find out about medicine?

(5, 17, 34)

2 What two subjects can you find out about on page 27?

(bathing and hygiene, Dalmatians and puppies, accidents and bones)

2

Answer these questions.

3 This index is for a book. What do you think that book is about?

_____

4 Which letters of the alphabet before 'p' do not have an entry in this index? _____

Copy these words into the table below under the subjects you might find them in.

rod   **mixing bowl**   **dried fruit**   **maggots**

waterproof clothing   **oven**

5–10

Fishing	Cooking

6

Circle the **pronoun(s)** in each sentence.

11 Ali passed him the ball.

12–13 We saw her at the shops.

14 The scarf looked like hers.

4

Finish the two sentences.

15 When will _____

16 What does _____

2

Write two words that begin with *ch*.

17–18 _____   _____

Write two words that end with *ch*.

4

19–20 _____   _____

20
TOTAL

The Lion and the Mouse

Beneath the spreading baobab,
the lion slept.

Mouse scuttled over parched earth,
climbed unwittingly the sandy mound
then saw – too late.
Fresh from hungry dreams
the lion awoke
and snatched the mouse.

Spare me, free me, please!
begged Mouse.
*Oh, wise and strong and tall,
lord of all hunters,
king of all creatures;
your strength and power are great,
my strength is small ...*

*Save me, spare my life, I pray!
Though I am weak, I know,
I promise that one day
I will repay you.
Let me go!*

The lion roared with mirth.
*You, repay me?
You, one of the smallest on the earth ...?
We'll see!*

Yet, shaking still with mirth,
he set him free.

The mouse walked free –
but not the lion.
When next they met
the lion, whimpering in despair,
lay tangled in a hunter's net,
roped to a tree.

At last, my turn!
cried grateful Mouse.
*Now I can keep my promise,
just you see!*

And patiently he bit and gnawed,
he gnawed and bit until, at last,
the net was opened up:

the lion was free!

By Judith Nicholls

Underline the right answers.

 1 Why did the lion grab the mouse?

(he was hungry, he didn't like mice, he wanted to frighten the mouse)

 2 What is the lion 'king' of?

(hunters, creatures, all the weak)

2

Answer these questions.

 3 How did the mouse repay the lion for setting him free?

_____

_____

 4 What message does this poem give us about strong and weak things?

_____

_____

2

Add the missing words to the table.

5–9

Present tense (happening now)	Past tense (happened in the past)
dig	
give	
say	
tell	
grow	

5

Add *ee* or *ea* to spell each word correctly.

10 sl_____p

11 str_____m

12 sh_____p

13 scr_____m

4

Copy these book titles adding the missing capital letters.

14 the river thames

_____

15 jack dresses up!

_____

16 dinosaurs in water

_____

3

Draw lines to match the **antonyms**.

17 clean   open

18 hard   run

19 shut   dirty

20 walk   soft

4

20
TOTAL

Paper 15

ink	a coloured liquid used for writing and printing
insect	a small animal with six legs
instrument	(1) a tool used for a job
	(2) something you play to make music
Jj	
jar	a container, usually made of glass
jaw	the lower part of your face, below your mouth
jeans	trousers made from a strong cotton material
jelly	a clear food that wobbles
jellyfish	a creature that lives in the sea and looks a bit like jelly
jerk	a quick, sudden movement
jet	a very fast aircraft
jewel	a precious stone, such as a diamond
jewellery	the name for ornaments people wear, such as rings and necklaces

Underline the right answers.

1 What has six legs?

(a jerk, a jellyfish, an insect)

2 Which word has two definitions?

(jewellery, jaw, instrument)

`2`

Answer these questions.

3 What is the last word in the dictionary that begins with 'i'?

_____

4 Which word means a sudden movement?

_____

`2`

Write a question that each statement answers.

Example   Sarah had baked beans for tea.
What did Sarah have for tea?

5 Statement: Brian went swimming at 3 o'clock.

_____

6 Statement: Alice went to Mark's house for tea.

_____

7 Statement: Mum wore a red jumper on Tuesday.

_____

8 Statement: The school fête is on 16th May.

_____

Add the **suffix** *ful* to these words.

9 help   + ful = _____

10 pain   + ful = _____

11 care   + ful = _____

12 wonder + ful = _____

Write these words in **alphabetical order**.

walk   **swim**   **run**   **crawl**

13 (1) _____   14 (2) _____

15 (3) _____   16 (4) _____

Underline the **proper noun** in each sentence.

17 Yasmin enjoyed swimming.

18 We went to Birmingham.

19 Jess lives in a caravan.

20 I went to visit my grandparents in India.

Paper 16

George had just started school. At the beginning of the week he was in the reception class, by the end he was in Year 6. George was a very talented child, in fact he was top of the top class. At the end of his first week at school he went to bed saying he felt tired ...
suddenly there was an awful wailing coming from his bedroom.

"I'm coming, my baby!" called George's mother. "Mummy's coming!" and she rushed upstairs to find George sitting up in bed, sobbing his heart out. This was not the confident self-assured know-it-all cleverest child in the school. This was just a frightened baby, and she cuddled him as fiercely as she had when he was only tiny and had never spoken a word. "What is it, George darling?" she said as she mopped away his tears. "Did you have a bad dream?"

"I did, I did Mummy!" sobbed George.

"What was it? Tell Mummy."

Gradually George's sobs turned to sniffles, and then he blew his nose and said, "I dreamt we were doing a science test at school."

"A science test?"

"Yes, we do science in the new curriculum, you know. And there was a simple question in it that I couldn't answer, and I cried like a baby. I cried in the dream, and I was crying when I woke up. I really must apologise for behaving so childishly."

"Poor lamb!" said his mother. "What was the question?"

"It was the order of events in the cycle of the internal combustion engine," said George.

"Forget about it, George," said his mother sadly. "I expect that there'll be lots of questions you won't know the answers to."

"Not if I can help it," said George.

"Anyway, don't worry. Just go back to sleep. Mummy's here."

"Oh, I shan't worry any more, Mother," said George in his usual confident tones. "I've remembered it now. It's Induction - Compression - Ignition - Exhaust," and exhausted, he lay back and went happily to sleep.

From *George Starts School* by Dick King-Smith

Underline the right answers.

1 What test did George dream about?

(maths test, spelling test, science test)

2 Why did George apologise to his mother?

(for not knowing the answer, for waking up, for behaving childishly) | 2 |

Answer these questions.

3–4 Write two words that could be used to describe George.

_____   _____ | 2 |

5–6 Write two reasons why you think George was exhausted when 'he lay back and went happily to sleep'.

(1) _____

(2) _____ | 2 |

Write the **plural** of each of these words.

7 boot _____   8 jumper _____

9 farm _____   10 lamp _____ | 4 |

Add the missing commas to this sentence.

11–12 The horse jumped over the gate the hay bail Jacob's bike and then escaped onto the road. | 2 |

Underline the **verb** in each of these sentences.

13 Fiona swam for forty minutes.

14 Tuhil kicked his ball hard.

15 The ducklings waddled onto the grass.

16 Lara lost her homework. | 4 |

Write these sentences in the correct order.

Then he found the robe he lost last year.

Once upon a time a king lost his crown.

In the end he found his crown; he had left it in the bathroom!

While he was searching he found his glasses.

17 (1) _____

_____

18 (2) _____

_____

19 (3) _____

_____

20 (4) _____

_____

4

20
TOTAL

Paper 17

The Life Cycle of a Frog

A frog lays some eggs.

The egg is protected by a jelly-like material.

The tail-bud begins to grow.

The tadpole wriggles free and attaches to some weed.

The back legs begin to grow.

Then the front legs grow.

After about eleven weeks the frog

is fully grown and can leave the water.

Underline the right answers.

1 What is the egg protected by?

   (the frog, pond weed, a jelly-like material)

2 Which legs grow first?

   (the front legs, the back legs)

2

Answer these questions.

3 About how many weeks does it take an egg to grow into a frog?

   _____

4 Why do you think the tadpole attaches to some weed when it leaves
   the jelly-like material?

   _____

   _____

2

Write a word with *ai* or *ay* to match each picture.

5 _____   6 _____

7 _____   8 _____

4

Write a question sentence starting with each of these words.

9 Where _____

10 When _____

11 What _____

12 Which _____

4

Find the four words in the wordsearch and write them in the spaces below.

Clue: each word can be found in a classroom.

13–16

t	r	o	l	p	x	a	g
g	t	e	a	c	h	e	r
p	a	i	n	t	l	b	j
s	b	d	u	r	p	o	r
w	l	h	y	r	s	o	s
z	e	g	j	r	u	k	m

_____

_____

_____

_____

4

Write each of these words in a sentence.

17 **before**

_____

18 **next**

_____

19 **during**

_____

20 **meanwhile**

_____

4

20
TOTAL

Magic Cat

My mum whilst walking through the door
Spilt some magic on the floor.
Blobs of this
and splots of that
but most of it upon the cat.

Our cat turned magic, straight away
and in the garden went to play
where it grew two massive wings
and flew around in fancy rings.
'Oh look!' cried Mother, pointing high,
I didn't know our cat could fly.'
Then with a dash of Tibby's tail
she turned my mum into a snail!
So now she lives beneath a stone
and dusts around a different home.
And I'm an ant
and Dad's a mouse
And Tibby's living in our house.

By Peter Dixon

Underline the right answers.

1 What did the cat grow when the magic spilt on her?

(big wings, big whiskers, a big tail)

2 Who lives in the house at the end of the poem?

(Dad, the snail, the cat)

2

Answer these questions.

3 Find a word in the poem that means the same as 'under'.

_____

4 Do you think Tibby liked having the magic spilt on her? Why?

_____

_____

2

Copy these book titles, adding the missing capital letters.

5 school stories

_____

6 the badger's bath

_____

7 famous people in history

_____

8 growing a sunflower

_____ `4`

Add the **prefix** _dis_ to each word to make its **antonym**.

9 _____like   **10** _____obey

11 _____appear   **12** _____trust   `4`

Write three words you would use to write about each of these topics.

13 school   _____   _____   _____

14 football   _____   _____   _____

15 weddings   _____   _____   _____

16 art   _____   _____   _____   `4`

Fill each gap with a word in the **present tense**. Use words in bold to help.

Example   The boy is _walking_. **walk**

17 The cats are _____ .   **fight**

18 Jake is _____ his ruler.   **bend**

19 The boys are _____ the ball.   **throw**

20 Aimee is _____ her Dad.   **help**   `4`

`20`
TOTAL

Paper 19

Faces

Look in the mirror. Which part of your body do you see?
Probably, your face. This is the most-looked-at part of anybody's body,
for many reasons.

Faces are truly fascinating. They show people's moods – happy, sad,
pleased, worried, tired or thoughtful. Tiny movements of the eyebrows
and eyelids can mean a lot, like surprise or anger. A flicker around
the lips may mean that a smile is coming, or a frown.

In most countries a nod of the head indicates yes, and a shake
means no.

When we listen to people speak, we also watch the movements of
their mouths and lips. This helps us to make out what they say. Also,
the rest of the body is often covered by clothes, so you cannot see it!

How faces change with age

As you grow, your face gets bigger. It also changes its proportions.
A baby's face is small compared to the size of its whole head. Its
eyes and forehead are big, its nose and mouth are small. In a
grown-up, the nose and mouth take up more of the face. And the face
takes up more than half of the front of the head.

From *Learn About The Body* by Steve Parker

Underline the right answers.

1 In most countries, what does a shake of the head mean?

   (yes, no)

2 What feature is small on a baby's face?

   (eyes, nose, forehead)

2

Answer these questions.

3 Write another mood your face might show that isn't listed above.

_____

4 Give a reason why your face is the most-looked-at part of your body.

_____

Circle a **noun** and underline a **verb** in each sentence.

5–6 The dog swam in the river.

7–8 We ate some sweets.

9–10 They jumped onto the wall.

Only copy the words which have been said.

11 "We must put our coats on," said Hannah.

_____

12 "Where is my hat?" asked Nazar.

_____

13 "It is cold outside," warned Jack.

_____

Answer the clues using a *wh* or *ph* word from the box.

elephant	dolphin	wheel	white

14 I am grey and swim.   _____

15 I help things move from one place to another.   _____

16 I am very big and usually live in hot places.   _____

17 I am a colour.   _____

Write a **synonym** for each word.

18 quick _____   **19 chew** _____

20 shout _____

The Owl and the Pussy-Cat

The Owl and the Pussy-Cat went to sea
In a beautiful pea-green boat,
They took some honey, and plenty of money,
Wrapped up in a five-pound note.
The Owl looked up to the stars above,
And sang to a small guitar,
'O lovely Pussy! O Pussy, my love,
What a beautiful Pussy you are,
You are,
You are!
What a beautiful Pussy you are!'

Pussy said to the Owl, 'You elegant fowl!
How charmingly sweet you sing!
O let us be married! too long have we tarried:
But what shall we do for a ring?'
They sailed away for a year and a day,
To the land where the Bong-tree grows,
And there in a wood a Piggy-wig stood
With a ring at the end of his nose,
His nose,
His nose,
With a ring at the end of his nose.

'Dear Pig, are you willing to sell for one shilling
Your ring?' Said the Piggy, 'I will.'
So they took it away, and were married next day
By the Turkey who lives on the hill.
They dined on mince and slices of quince,
Which they ate with a runcible spoon;
And hand in hand, on the edge of the sand,
They danced by the light of the moon,
The moon,
The moon,
They danced by the light of the moon.

By Edward Lear

Underline the right answers.

ı For how much did the Piggy-wig sell his ring?
(one shilling, five shillings, five pounds)

2 Where does the Turkey live?
(on the beach, on the hill, in a wood)

2

Answer these questions.

3 Why did the Owl and the Pussy-Cat want the Piggy's ring?

_____

_____

4 Which verse of this poem do you like the best? Why?

_____

_____

_____

2

Put these words in **alphabetical order**.

pizza	curry	sausages	mushrooms

5 (1) _____   **6** (2) _____

7 (3) _____   **8** (4) _____

4

Copy and add the missing punctuation to each sentence.

9–11 Please come to my house for tea said Clare

_____

12–14 When shall I come to tea asked Jess

_____

6

Underline the part of each word that sounds the same.

15–17 bird   purse   nerve

3

Circle the **pronouns** in these sentences.

18 I went to the shop.   **19** They ate bananas.   **20** Can we go swimming?

3

20
TOTAL